# Fontaine Fox's

# TOONERVILLE TROLLEY

# Fontaine Fox's
# TOONERVILLE TROLLEY

THE TOONERVILLE TROLLEY THAT MEETS ALL THE TRAINS
FLEM PRODDY, THE LOCAL INVENTOR, OFTEN BOARDS THE
CAR IN THAT DEEP CUT EAST OF TOWN

MAKE UP YER MIND! A FREE RIDE TO TOWN OR OVER SHE GOES!

EXPERT MECHANIC

GAS

Compiled by

*Herb Galewitz & Don Winslow*

WEATHERVANE BOOKS • NEW YORK

## Acknowledgment

Some of the cartoons herein were photographed from a collection held by the Lilly Library in Bloomington, Indiana. We wish to thank that organization and especially Miss Elfrieda Lang, Curator of Manuscripts, for their courtesy and help.

The balance of cartoons was assembled from those "zany, oddball" collectors who have been clipping and saving newspaper cartoons since the days of Opper and Swinnerton. With their help, the history of comic art becomes an exciting and stimulating voyage. Thank you, fellows.

# Contents

# Introduction

Remember when vacant lots abounded in our land and kids played on them the year round?  Remember when trolley cars crisscrossed every street and some lines ended in the "country"? Remember tomboys, when that term was used without reference to a sexual aberration? Remember chaperones, and when elderly people were a vigorous part of the community? Remember when suburbia could be located only a few miles from downtown?

Fontaine T. Fox did and he recorded that era faithfully and humorously in his marvelous *Toonerville Folks* cartoons that ran for over forty years.

The humor highlighted the idiosyncrasies of the Toonerville populace. Their individual traits were spotlighted and brought into sharp focus in the daily gag panels. There were no John Does. Everyone had a "handle," a nickname to alert one to the humorous possibilities. You weren't just *Mr. Flint,* but rather *Banker Flint* or *Old Man Flint.* Fox, of course, didn't start this. He just continued the practice that goes back to the Middle Ages and possibly before. Nowadays, the use of nicknames is diminishing. (Don't tell me about Billy, Dick and Bobby. They don't count.) Our teachers and parents claimed that nicknames weren't nice. They were vulgar and made fun of people. The authorities were quite right, but then again, if you were just a fellow who loved to overeat, you didn't go through life as another blob, but rather as "Fat." You had your position in the order of things. It might take a while to get used to the appellation, but by then you had an identity. Isn't that worth the torment?

Fox used the "handles" as they were appropriate to the times. After all, he was giving us a look at a period of American life, and he gave it to us warts and all.

When Fox's father, a judge and editorial writer, saw his son's first published cartoon in the *Louisville Herald,* he thundered, ". . . it's a mighty queer way to make a living," and stormed out of the room much in the manner of the Terrible Tempered Mr. Bang. If he used the word "queer" in the sense of being unique, then Mr. Fox, Sr., was indeed prophetic. At the height of their popularity, the cartoons of Fontaine Fox appeared in almost three hundred newspapers, daily and Sunday. Toys, games, books, movies, and ads (Vaseline, for one) were issued featuring the singular Toonerville characters. In 1933, the black heart of the Depression, *Fortune* magazine estimated that Fox's income from newspaper syndication alone was $1,400 a week.

One famous child star tried to cash in on the popularity of Mickey (Himself) McGuire, Fox's tough Irish kid, and adopted his name for a series of films. Fox sued and actor Joe Yule, Jr., again changed his name, this time to Mickey Rooney.

That first published cartoon was political and came after two ventures into straight reporting had ended in near disaster. Fox, just out of Louisville's Boys' High School, was sent to spy on a secret nudist colony. An irate member discovered him, and with a right to the jaw sent the cub reporter fleeing. Later, he was sent to a local racetrack to sketch a local sportsman with a celebrated hooked nose. The artwork was too accurate and Fox again had to flee the swipes of the cane-wielding gentleman.

In 1904, Fox went to Indiana University and, in his second year on campus, supported himself by sending a cartoon a day to the *Louisville Herald* for $12 a week. However, he had to put the finished drawing each night on the 1:10 A.M. train to ensure its safe arrival in Kentucky. After one year of moonlighting, Fox left the university to return to Louisville as a full-time cartoonist and sketch artist for the *Times.* He also had more time to play baseball, which he had excelled in during high school and college days. Now, he joined a semi-pro team, the Dusty Rhodes, which played in the west end of Louisville. The senior Fox frowned on Sunday baseball, so young Fontaine told him that he spent the Sabbath visiting a girl who lived on a farm in Indiana. He actually did go to see the girl, but only on those days when the ballgame was rained out. The girl's farmer father was always glad to see Fox as when he came he brought the welcome rain.

After four years of sharpening his art technique on political and topical subjects, Fox accepted an offer to work on the *Chicago Post.* The king of cartoonists in Chicago at that time was John McCutcheon of the *Tribune.* He did political, topical, and general atmospheric work much in the vein of his fellow Hoosier and poet, James Whitcomb Riley.

McCutcheon was one of the first cartoonists to use children in his art and they were very popular. Therefore, when Fox approached his managing editor, Leigh Reilly, for permission to do humorous cartoons of children to break up the steady diet of political work, the reply was that McCutcheon was already doing it and how dare he [Fox] compete with the acknowledged master in his own town! Fox pointed out that McCutcheon's kids were in the Tom Sawyer country mold, while his kids would come from that new area of population growth, the suburbs.

Reilly relented and let Fox try a few. The first one showed a mother and a small boy waiting for a streetcar. (A symbol of things to come!) As the car appeared, the mother discovered that the boy had wandered into a vacant lot, where he found a derby and was trying it on. The last panel was set in a barbershop, where the boy's hair is being shampooed and his stern mother looks on. The editor liked the strip and printed it on the front page, and put Fox on a one-a-week humorous cartoon schedule.

By 1915, Fox had joined the Wheeler Syndicate and his national success was launched. He moved to New York, the headquarters for the Syndicate, and started to enlarge his stock cast of characters, which now included *Thomas Edison, Jr., Sissie,* and *Grandma, the Demon Chaperone.*

Fox, like most other cartoonists, relied on everyday events and ordinary people as source material for his gags and characters. His most famous creation was inspired by a friendly old bearded motorman who ran a rundown trolley in Pelham, New York. Fox had traveled on his line on a visit to cartoonist Charlie Voight's home. (Voight is best remembered for his comic strip *Betty.*) By the time Fox returned to his own home, he had recalled another rundown trolley line in Louisville, the Brook Street run. He merged the two lines into *The Toonerville Trolley That Meets All Trains* and its conductor-motorman, the Skipper. It was an immediate success.

Fox credited his own father as the prototype for *the Terrible Tempered Mr. Bang,* but Mrs. Fox claimed that Fox himself was the original Mr. Bang. Fox readily admitted that he used Mr. Bang as an outlet for his pet peeves. For example, Fox once went to a movie where he paid his admission. Inside he was informed by the usher that there would be a wait for seats. Fox fumed, but like most of us said nothing. But the next day he drew a cartoon of Mr. Bang in the same situation, who reacted by grabbing the usher by the seat of his pants and airborning him to the outside of the theater to make an announcement that there were no seats inside.

*Mickey McGuire* and *The Little Scorpions* were replicas of boyhood chums in Louisville.

*The Powerful Katrinka* was a combination of a black female cook who worked for Fox's father and Ole Olson, a football character out of a George Fitch novel.

For art inspiration, the young Fox turned to John Leech, the great British caricaturist. He found his illustrations in *Comic History of England* (1848) by Gilbert Abbott à Beckett. Though the styles of Leech and Fox are about as unrelated as any two artists, Fox did attribute his early knowledge of expression to a study of that book. Fox's scratchy style is deceptively simple. Though at times he had assistants to help with the backgrounds, Fox could never find anyone to draw the characters to his own satisfaction. Once Fox had the subject idea, the drawing was done quite rapidly, and at the same time he accompanied himself by singing a few stanzas of those turn-of-the-century mournful ballads, "The Baggage Coach Ahead" or "The Browns Have Lost Their Baby Boy." Luckily, the songs never pervaded the art.

*Toonerville Folks* reached the end of the line on February 9, 1955, when the seventy-year-old Fox retired to Florida. Wisely, neither the Syndicate nor Fox sought a replacement. The "vacant lot" era of American life was disappearing. It was beaten by the population explosion of post-World War II, suburban developers, and urban blight. Today, seventeen years later, we have "progressed" to professional Little Leagues, artificial grass, and the disappearance of street life. It is enough to make a grown man cry.

Fontaine Fox died August 9, 1964, in Greenwich, Connecticut.

Herb Galewitz

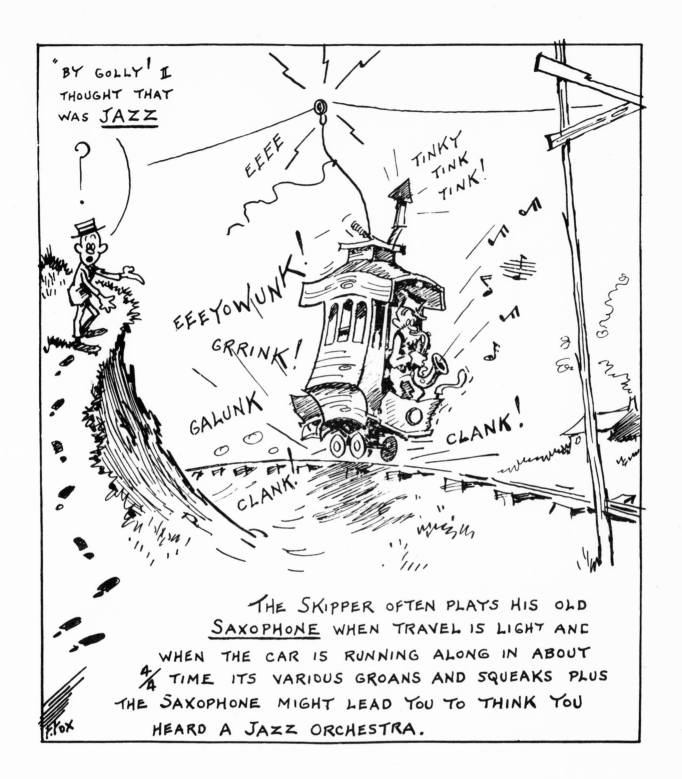

2

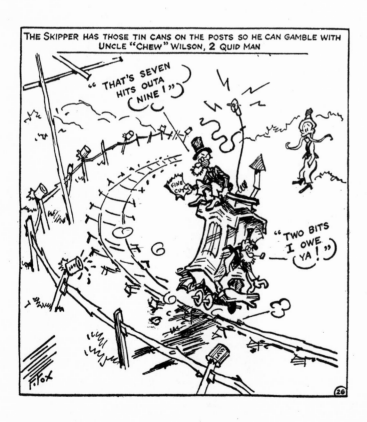

6

8

WHERE THE TRANSIT COMMISSION HAS FAILED TO MAKE THE SKIPPER REMOVE THAT "PAINTER'S" SCAFFOLD, THE YOUNG FOLKS WILL PROBABLY SUCCEED

THE SKIPPER STILL INSISTS THAT LEM WORTLE CUT THE ROPE WHICH HELD THAT LOAD OF FURNITURE ON THE "PAINTER'S." SCAFFOLD

"IT'S A SORT OF A 'DRAW BRIDGE' ARRANGEMENT HE HINGES ON DURING THE JANUARY THAW!"

" GO ON AND TAKE ONE O' THEM PACKAGES AND BEAT IT BEFORE HE COMES TO HE'S GOT SO MUCH STUFF HE'D NEVER MISS IT ENNYWAY !"

WHEN THE MEN WHO CAME OUT ON THE 4:15 FOUND THAT THE OLD SKIPPER HAD REPAIRED THAT BROKEN WINDOW WITH A BRAND NEW PANE OF GLASS —

THE SKIPPER RAN WHAT YOU MIGHT CALL A "SIGHT SEEING EXCURSION" DOWN TO GOOSE CRICK LAST WEEK AND CLEANED UP A CONSIDERABLE SUM IN FARES BESIDES HIS ARRESTING FEE AS CONSTABLE.

The Skipper carries a Key to any vacant houses along the line and never passes up a chance to pick up a small real estate commission

THE BACK PLATFORM FELL OFF AGAIN LAST WEEK AND THE SKIPPER CAME SERENLY UP TO THE DEPOT WITHOUT EVEN KNOWING IT WAS GONE!

The Skipper is too good a fisherman himself not to hold up traffic for a few minutes in this sort of a situation.

When the car is about half filled and all passengers crowd over beside the car stove the skipper always refuses to go ahead until they right the old boat.

Ed Penny the new traffic officer at Dead Center, never HAS liked the skipper of the Trolley and is certainly making life miserable for him.

The Salesman presented the Skipper with a cigar in the hope of having him make quicker time to the depot but it produced just the OPPOSITE effect.

The Skipper's intimate knowledge of men, women and events in the district makes it possible for him to render both public and personal service on occasions.

Bert Eggers is too big to get inside the car and sit in the middle so when Bert is the only passenger the Skipper has to run the car in a rather *unusual* manner.

Ed Wortle has built himself a platform from which he can step right off onto the roof because by the time the car reaches his house every morning there ain't any other place to ride.

CROSSTIE INSPECTION

21

OFFICER MILLER, ARCH ENEMY OF MICKEY (HIMSELF) McGUIRE, WAS STRUCK ON THE HEAD BY A PIECE OF FLYING DEBRIS THE DAY OF THE BIG WIND.

MICKEY McGUIRE OFTEN HAS A GALLERY TO WATCH THE SHOTS HE MAKES DELIVERING THE AFTERNOON PAPERS

WHEN MICKEY McGUIRE STEPS ON THE SCALES UP AT THE CORNER DRUG STORE

"IF HE'S OVERWEIGHT HE'LL BE LOOKIN' FOR EXERCISE AND YA KNOW WOT THAT MEANS!"

THE FAT BOY THAT MICKEY McGUIRE HAS BEEN "AFTER"

"HIS MA TOLD ME TO FIND HIM AND BRING HIM HOME AND I FOUND HIM WHERE HE WAS HIDIN' FROM THAT McGUIRE BOY!"

"AND HE'S STUCK."

45

# THE TERRIBLE TEMPERED MR. BANG & THE PAPER NAPKIN

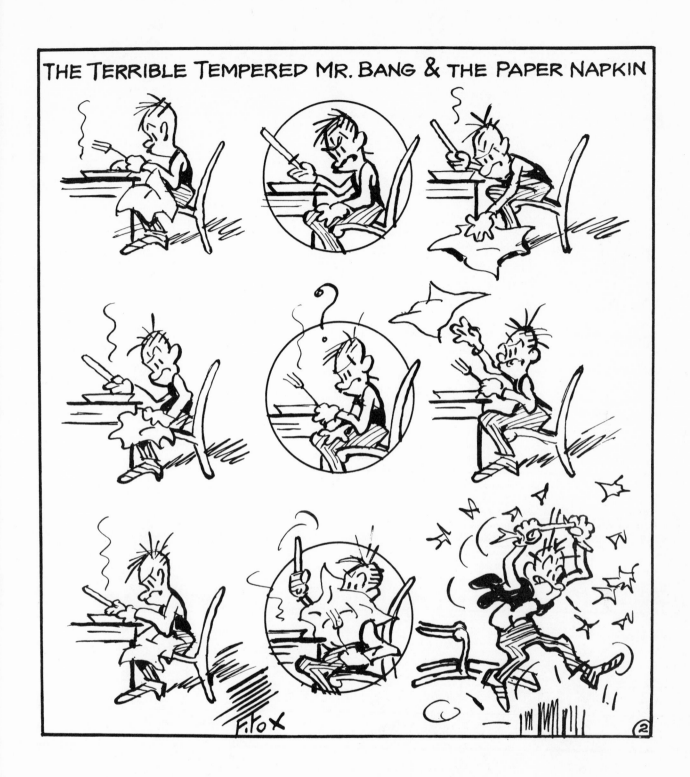

50

THE TERRIBLE TEMPERED MR. BANG
WINDS UP AN ARGUMENT ABOUT GEN. PATTON

.... AND I ALSO ADMIRE HIS METHODS!

A SMALL CROWD USUALLY COLLECTS TO WATCH MR. BANG SPLIT KINDLING TO START UP THE FURNACE WHEN "THOSE FOOL WOMEN HAVE SAT THERE ALL AFTERNOON AND LET THE FIRE GO OUT"!

THE TERRIBLE TEMPERED MR. BANG
GOES OVER WITH SOME EMPTY MILK BOTTLES TO WHERE
THE MILKMAN DOES HIS SLEEPING IN THE DAYTIME

THE TERRIBLE TEMPERED MR. BANG

EVERY MONTH THERE'S ALWAYS SOME ONE BILL THAT HAS THAT AFFECT UPON HIM!

UNCLE EPH WORTLE HAD FIGURED ON A LONGER SKIRT

NOT EVEN THE DOCTOR CAN KEEP POP WORTLE, THE OLD STRING SAVER, IN BED DURING KITE SEASON

EPH WORTLE READ IN THE PAPER THAT COWS GIVE MORE MILK WITH A RADIO IN THE BARN

JED WORTLE JUST CAN'T GET ALONG WITH CITY FOLKS

64

BEARDSLEY WORTLE
DURING THE BRUSH FIRE SEASON WHEN THERE ARE SO MANY SPARKS FLYING THROUGH THE AIR

EVENT OF THE WEEK
BEARDSLEY WORTLE WAS CAUGHT IN THE SUDDEN FREEZE FOLLOWING A COLD RAIN

EVENT OF THE MONTH!
CURT SIMS' ELDEST DAUGHTER AND RUFUS WORTLE'S SON FINALLY REACH THE HAND-HOLDING STAGE.

WHILE WE'RE ON THE SUBJECT OF ALL-AMERICAN PASS RECEIVERS, HOW ABOUT THAT GOOD LOOKIN' WORTLE GAL!

OTHERS MAY WALK IN THEIR SLEEP, BUT FATS WORTLE (THE AMAZING COMMUTER) RUNS

MISS AMY WORTLE'S BOARDING HOUSE

SO THAT'S HOW THEY FOLLOW EACH OTHER INTO THE BATHROOM WITH US WAITING RIGHT OUTSIDE THE DOOR!

POP WORTLE, THE OLD STRING SAVER, WAS ASKED WHAT SORT OF A CHRISTMAS HE HAD

ABE WORTLE'S YOUNGEST BOY IS SIX AND A HALF FEET TALL AND ONLY FOURTEEN YEARS OLD

FESTUS WORTLE IS THE MOST WIDELY TRAVELED MAN IN THE WHOLE TOWNSHIP

PROSSER WORTLE HAS HAD HIS WIFE'S MA AND PA, HIS OWN MA, AND HIS MA'S TWO SISTERS LIVING WITH THEM FOR YEARS

MOTHER WOULD PROBABLY HAVE THROWN A DUCK FIT IF SHE COULD HAVE SEEN KATRINKA AND THE BABY GOING OVER TO THE ICE PLANT FIRE.

SEVERAL PEOPLE GATHERED OUTSIDE THE WINDOW TO RUBBER AT HER AND ALL SHE WAS DOING WAS LOOKING AT SOME COLORED PICTURES IN THE DICTIONARY.

IT WILL BE MANY A DAY BEFORE MOTHER LETS HER PUT ANOTHER LETTER IN THE MAIL BOX WITHOUT LEAVING THE CAR.

KATRINKA!

"THAT BAG! THE POWERFUL KATRINKA CANT LIFT THAT BAG! WANTA BET A DOLLAR SHE CANT?

YEP!

"I DONT NOTICE HER LIFTING IT ANY

FIRE PLUG!

The Powerful Katrinka can amuse a child in more different ways!

The Powerful Katrinka

The sweat bees kept bothering the Powerful Katrinka while she was rolling the lawn

The Powerful Katrinka was asked to bring in the new tennis net

THE POWERFUL KATRINKA'S FOLKS ARE GETTING THEIR HOUSE-BOAT AROUND WITH NO GAS WHATSOEVER

S'NUF!

THE POWERFUL (PHYSICALLY) KATRINKA
IT'S TO MAKE IT EASIER TO CARRY WOOD FOR THE FIREPLACE

THE POWERFUL KATRINKA
CHARGES SUMMER HOTELKEEPERS A REGULAR FEE OF 50¢ FOR SHAKING HANDS WITH PERPETUAL PIANO PLAYERS

EVENT OF THE WEEK
TINWARE SALESMAN PUTS HIS FOOT IN THE POWERFUL KATRINKA'S KITCHEN DOOR

*The professor will never be able to fish successfully as long as he has any sort of a book with him.*

By FONTAINE FOX.

EVENT OF THE WEEK
"SKYSCRAPER" SMITH BUSTED ANOTHER STREET LIGHT!

"SKYSCRAPER" SMITH IS WORKING OUT BY THE DAY

ONLY TROUBLE IS I HAFTA LUG MY OWN DURN GARDEN TOOLS!

EVENT OF THE WEEK—"SKYSCRAPER" SMITH LOSES HIS TEMPER

BUT I KEEP TELLIN' YA I DON'T WANTA GO TO THE BIG CITY AND LEARN TO PLAY BASKETBALL!

"SKYSCRAPER" SMITH AND THE APRIL FOOL SIGN

—EVERYTHING IS SO HIGH THESE DAYS!

KICK ME HERE

STOR

"THEY'LL HAFTA GET A STEP LADDER OR BACK HIM UP AGAINST A TALL STUMP!"

## AUNT EPPIE HOGG
### HAS NEVER BEEN ABLE TO GET INSIDE THE LOCAL MOVIE.

## WHY AUNT EPPIE HOGG BECAME A VEGETARIAN

## EVENT OF THE WEEK
### OLD MAN FISHER AND HIS FAMOUS FLIVVER CRASH INTO AUNT EPPIE HOGG

AUNT EPPIE HOGG, THE WORLD'S MOST EFFICIENT PICKET

AUNT EPPIE HOGG, WITHOUT AN AUTO, STILL HAS TO CONTEND WITH HITCH-HIKERS

AUNT EPPIE HOGG NEVER DID LIKE THE TRUANT OFFICER ANYHOW

AUNT EPPIE HOGG, THE FATTEST WOMAN IN 3 COUNTIES

# THE POWERFUL KATRINKA & HER SWEETHEART, THE DWARF

Using a bucket of bran to lead the Cow onward, Tomboy Taylor carries out her threat to wreck the club-house after the members had black balled her just because she was a girl.

Three members were "kicked out of the club" last week. More members would have been kicked out if more had been in it when Tomboy Taylor's gang descended on THE PLACE.

It seems as though whenever Tomboy decides to pull off one of her stunts (such as walking out to the end of the spring board on stilts) then is the very time her mother will happen along.

When her mother left the flivver, Tomboy seized the opportunity to give an exhibition of modern dancing.

*Tomboy Taylor felt that if she jumped to the floor it would shake things down so that she could eat some more turkey.*      *By Fontaine Fox.*

GRANDMA FUTTY CERTAINLY KNOWS HOW TO HANDLE 'EM

GRANDMA FUTTY HAS A PAIR OF GRAY SLACKS FOR SALE

THE GRANDMA FUTTY SPECIAL PUTTER IS SELLING VERY WELL

GRANDMA FUTTY FIGHTS INFLATION

110

### THAT FAMOUS MID-MORNING GAME THE KICKOFF (A LA GRANDMA FUTTY)

### GRANDMA'S CANE IS A FEARSOME WEAPON OF MANY USES.

### GRANDMA'S EYESIGHT MAKES HER A SUCKER FOR CAMOUFLAGE

### GRANDMA'S CANE IS A FEARFUL WEAPON, OF MANY USES

GRANDMA FUTTY

GRANDMA FUTTY CARRIES A LARGE WOODEN WHISTLE WITH HER WHEN SHE GOES SHOPPING

GRANDMA FUTTY'S
BLUE MONDAY MORNING MAGIC MIXTURE ☆

☆ THE WORLD'S WORST TASTING MEDICINE !

GRANDMA FUTTY IS ABOUT THE NEATEST HOUSEKEEPER IN TOWN

114

GRANPAW FUTTY BRINGS HOME A JUG OF RARE OLD LICKER ON A VERY SLIPPERY DAY

GRANPAW FUTTY HATES CITY FOLKS

JUST LIKE 'EM TO HOLD BACK WITH THEIR PRESENT-STYLE BATHING SUITS TILL MY EYESIGHT IS PRACTICALLY GONE!

EARLY MORNING GAME IN THE PARK

REMEMBER NOW, IF GRANPAW TOUCHES THE RUNNER WITH HIS CANE THE PLAY IS STOPPED!

GRANDPAW FUTTY
HAS BEEN DINING OUT WITH HIS DAUGHTER IN THE BIG CITY

IT'S A CLAMP! TO KEEP THEM DURN WAITERS FROM WHISKING MY PLATE AWAY WHEN I'M ONLY HALF FINISHED!

NOW IT CAN BE TOLD!

"THASS A GOOD ONE! BUT NOW THAT SHE'S GONE BACK TO THE CITY, LEMME TELL YA WOT THAT FAT WOMAN WOT BOARDED AT OUR HOUSE DID EVERY EVENING BEFORE SHE TOOK HER BATH~"

THEY HAVE A NAME FOR THE FRONT STEPS OF THE GENERAL STORE

"WHEN I PASSED HE WAS SITTING OVER THERE IN THE GRANDSTAND!"

WINDY DAY BOY SCOUT ESCORT PAST THAT NASTY OLD "GRANDSTAND"

ADD — RUBBER SHORTAGE

RIGHT IN FRONT OF THE GRANDSTAND AND NOT ONE O' THE BOYS SETTIN' THERE!

# PINCKNEY WORTLE,
## THE WORLD'S LAZIEST WHITE MAN, HAS A JOB!

129

131

"SNAG" SANDERS, TOONERVILLE'S FAMOUS MUSTACHE ARTIST, HAS HAD TO DISGUISE THAT 14-FOOT CRAYON HOLDER HE USES FOR BILL-BOARD WORK

"SNAG" SANDERS, TOONERVILLE'S FAMOUS MUSTACHE ARTIST, EXECUTES A MOST DARING PIECE OF WORK

LONGSTREET REACH

HAS SAVED MISS AMY WORTLE MANY A STEP DURING THE THIRTY-FIVE YEARS HE HAS LIVED AT HER BOARDING HOUSE

# "FLYTRAP" FINNEGAN, THE WORLD'S WORST CADDIE

## EVENT OF THE WEEK
"HAMS" HENDERSON WAVES AT HIS BEST GIRL AND BLOWS 3 HATS OFF

152

# UNCLE "CHEW" WILSON, 2-QUID MAN

154

MEETS THE KID WHO'S ALWAYS STICKING

HIS TONGUE OUT AT EVERYBODY

HE SURE IS RAISING HEK WITH THEM ½ DRESSED CITY WIMMIN!

OLE MAN EUSTIS HAS BEEN HAVING A LOT OF FUN
AROUND TOWN WITH A FAKE PIPE

## CURB ON INFLATION
ONLY EVIDENCE OF ANY AROUND THESE PARTS HAS BEEN
OLD MAN EUSTIS AND HIS CAMOUFLAGED BEAN SHOOTER

# "WILBERT!"

# "WILBERT!"

By cutting some holes in an old hat box, Vernon McNutt made a phone booth so he could talk with more privacy to his sweetie over the BOARDING-HOUSE phone

### EVENT OF THE WEEK
EZRA FAIRCHILD'S DAUGHTER RETURNED HOME FROM COLLEGE AND ANNOUNCED SHE WAS A COMMUNIST

HARDER!

### EXCITEMENT AT THE POST OFFICE
BANKER FLINT TRIES TO KEEP 'EM FROM PICKING UP A COMIC VALENTINE HE'D CRUMPLED AND THROWN AWAY

LOOKS LIKE A GAME OF SHINNY!

POST OFFICE

THE BIG WIND BLEW ENUF STUFF OVER AGAINST THE CLIFF ON HY TURKIN'S PLACE TO LAST 'EM A LIFETIME

ONE OF 'EM'S BOUND TO FIT.

HOT DAWG!

EVENT OF THE WEEK
OLD MAN FLINT GIVES HIS BROTHER-IN-LAW SOME FACE CARDS

"HEE-HAW" HOSKINS HAS A JOB IN THE BIG CITY

GRANPAW GRUMP SMOKES ALL DAY LONG

GRANDMA SIMS' BAD WEATHER HOOK-UP

"STUMPY" SANDERS,
BELIEVE IT OR NOT, CAN RIDE ON THE TROLLEY WITH
MORE SECURITY THAN MOST ABLE-BODIED PEOPLE.

GRANPAW FINK

"MY PROBLEM IS TO HIDE THIS DOGGONE HEAVY FLANNEL
UNION SUIT SO MY WIFE WON'T KNOW I'VE TOOK IT OFF!"

TACTLESS TILLIE TOMPKINS

IT'S STRAIGHT
UP THIS HILL !
JUST FOLLOW
YOUR NOSE !

I HAVEN'T HEARD
THAT COP'S MOTORCYCLE ENGINE
FOR QUITE A WHILE NOW.
I GUESS IT'LL BE
SAFE TO SPEED 'ER
UP AGAIN.

HOLDING ON
WITH ENGINE
SHUT OFF

MOTORCYCLE PATROLMAN, ERT WIMP, HAS
CAUGHT MANY A CITY FELLER THIS SUMMER WITH
A SLICK TRICK HE'S BEEN WORKING.

OLD MAN RENNIE SHOWS OFF A SATISFIED CUSTOMER

GREAT-GRANDPA BOTTS — Vs — TELEVISION

SURREALISTIC PORTRAIT OF GRANDPA BOTTS

THERE NEVER IS ANY DIFFICULTY RAISING 5¢ TO BUY A CIGAR FOR THE FAMOUS BARON BOXCAR TO SMOKE.

"SNEEZER" WILKINS, WORLD'S WORST HAY FEVER SUFFERER

POOR MISTER HENRY PECK!

UNCLE OTTO'S FAMOUS NOSE

EDDIE SIMS' MA KNOWS HOW TO DO THINGS

169

"THAT'S EDDIE WHOOZIS, HARVARD'S GREAT BLOCKING BACK!"

FARMER FENNEL HAS ADDED SOMETHING TO HIS ENJOYMENT OF THE GAME OF GOLF

ZEKE WINGFIELD'S OLDEST BOY IS RAISING CAIN ABOUT HAVING TO GO BACK TO SCHOOL AGAIN THIS YEAR

WILBERT THE WEEPER

172

THE SMITHS ARE MIGHTY PROUD OF THEIR NEW RUBBER-TIRED BALL-BEARING BABY CARRIAGE

"KNOBHEAD" NEWSOME, WHOSE WIFE IS TOONERVILLE'S BEST SHOT WITH A PLATE OR A TEA CUP

KIBBY (KIBITZER) SNOOP, WHO HAS STRAINED HIS NECK FOR 50 YEARS WATCHING OTHER PEOPLE PLAY GAMES

"SNIDE" SANDERS, THE FAMOUS GOAT-GETTER

WE FIGGER DRAINING THE BLOOD DOWN FROM HIS ARM AND HAND WILL SHRINK HIS THUMB SO IT'LL COME OUTA THERE

THE LONG SOUGHT SECRET OF PUTTING IS USUALLY DISCOVERED IN MIDWINTER, ALONG ABOUT MIDNIGHT

WELL, THAT'S A SURPRISE! I DIDN'T THINK YOU'D BE ABLE TO MAKE ETHERIDGE STOP BOUNCING HIS BALL AGAINST THE HOUSE!

PROPOSED NEW DRAFT AGES IN THE PAPER

THERE ON THE FRONT PAGE

BY HEK! THIS'LL BE THE 4TH WAR I BIN IN!

178

NOT "MOTHERS' DAY" OR "FATHERS' DAY" BUT "GOOD FOR NOTHING UNCLES' DAY" IS THE BIG DAY, LOCALLY

ANNUAL PARADE

EVENT OF THE WEEK— THE SCRAP METAL PILE IN MONUMENT CIRCLE AT EAST SCURVEE WAS STRUCK BY LIGHTNING

FIND THE MAN WHOSE YOUNGSTER HAS GOT INTO THE CELLAR AND DRAGGED OUT MOST OF HIS "HOOCH" DISTILLING APPARATUS

He has been just about ready to give up the job ever since his wife hit on that idea of fastening the signals onto her churn handle.